the
gratitude
journal

FOR TEEN GIRLS

The Gratitude Journal for Teen Girls

this journal belongs to:

_____

gratitude guidelines:

Hey there! We're so glad you picked up this book. We've broken down the different aspects of this journal to help you get the most out of the 90 days of gratitude ahead of you. Each day you will find the following 4 sections:

1. **today I'm grateful for...**
Jot down 3 things that you are feeling thankful for that day. Don't overthink it, just write the first 3 things that come to mind!

2. **daily celebration:**
We can find something to celebrate each day if we look hard enough. Take a moment to consider your day and what event is worth bringing attention to. Draw a picture or write about the experience and how it made you feel!

3. **today I felt...**
Your daily emotional check in. Check one of the boxes or write in your own.

4. **standout human of the day**
As easy as it sounds... Write the name of someone who did something exceptional, took care of a need or just someone who made you smile today!

Habits are best built by repetition and consistency. We suggest finding favorite spot in the house and show up there each day at the same time with your journal and pen.
We can't wait for you to get started.
Happy journaling!

start date:	completion date:

here we go

DATE: /   /

today I'm grateful for...

1. _____

2. _____

3. _____

daily celebration:

today I felt...

excited ◯

happy ◯

confused ◯

frustrated ◯

sad ◯

_____ ◯

standout human

_____

of the day

_____

today I'm grateful for...

1. _____

2. _____

3. _____

daily celebration:

today I felt...

excited ○

happy ○

confused ○

frustrated ○

sad ○

_____ ○

standout human of the day

DATE: /   /

today I'm grateful for...

1. _____

2. _____

3. _____

daily celebration:

today I felt...

excited ⭕

happy ⭕

confused ⭕

frustrated ⭕

sad ⭕

_____ ⭕

standout human

of the day

today I'm grateful for...

1. _____

2. _____

3. _____

daily celebration:

today I felt...

excited ○

happy ○

confused ○

frustrated ○

sad ○

_____ ○

standout human of the day

DATE: /   /

today I'm grateful for...

1. _____

2. _____

3. _____

daily celebration:

today I felt...

excited ◯

happy ◯

confused ◯

frustrated ◯

sad ◯

_____ ◯

standout human of the day

today I'm grateful for...

1. _____

2. _____

3. _____

daily celebration:

today I felt...

excited ◯

happy ◯

confused ◯

frustrated ◯

sad ◯

_____ ◯

standout human

of the day

DATE: /   /

today I'm grateful for...

1. _____

2. _____

3. _____

daily celebration:

today I felt...

excited ◯

happy ◯

confused ◯

frustrated ◯

sad ◯

_____ ◯

standout human

of the day

today I'm grateful for...

1. _____

2. _____

3. _____

daily celebration:

today I felt...

excited ◯

happy ◯

confused ◯

frustrated ◯

sad ◯

_____ ◯

standout human
of the day

DATE: / /

today I'm grateful for...

1. _____
2. _____
3. _____

daily celebration:

today I felt...

excited ◯
happy ◯
confused ◯
frustrated ◯
sad ◯
_____ ◯

standout human
_____
of the day

today I'm grateful for...

1. _____

2. _____

3. _____

daily celebration:

today I felt...

excited ◯

happy ◯

confused ◯

frustrated ◯

sad ◯

_____ ◯

standout human
of the day

thank
you

Who do you feel grateful for this week? Take a moment to sit down and write them a letter, send a text, or give them a call to tell them how you feel. Making a habit of saying 'thank you' is one of the easiest ways to cultivate gratitude in our lives.

Challenge yourself to say 'thank you' to at least 1 person every day this week.

DATE: /   /

today I'm grateful for...

1. _____

2. _____

3. _____

daily celebration:

today I felt...

excited   ◯

happy   ◯

confused   ◯

frustrated   ◯

sad   ◯

_____ ◯

standout human

of the day

today I'm grateful for...

1. _____

2. _____

3. _____

daily celebration:

today I felt...

excited ○

happy ○

confused ○

frustrated ○

sad ○

_____ ○

standout human
of the day

DATE: /   /

today I'm grateful for...

1. _____

2. _____

3. _____

daily celebration:

today I felt...

excited ◯

happy ◯

confused ◯

frustrated ◯

sad ◯

_____ ◯

standout human

of the day

today I'm grateful for...

1. _____

2. _____

3. _____

daily celebration:

today I felt...

excited   ◯

happy   ◯

confused   ◯

frustrated   ◯

sad   ◯

_____   ◯

standout human

of the day

DATE: _____ / _____ / _____

today I'm grateful for...

1. _____

2. _____

3. _____

daily celebration:

today I felt...

excited ◯

happy ◯

confused ◯

frustrated ◯

sad ◯

_____ ◯

standout human

of the day

today I'm grateful for...

1. _____

2. _____

3. _____

daily celebration:

today I felt...

excited ○

happy ○

confused ○

frustrated ○

sad ○

_____ ○

standout human

of the day

DATE: / /

today I'm grateful for...

1. _____

2. _____

3. _____

daily celebration:

today I felt...

excited ◯

happy ◯

confused ◯

frustrated ◯

sad ◯

_____ ◯

standout human
_____
of the day

today I'm grateful for...

1. _____

2. _____

3. _____

daily celebration:

today I felt...

excited ⬭

happy ⬭

confused ⬭

frustrated ⬭

sad ⬭

_____ ⬭

standout human
of the day

DATE: / /

today I'm grateful for...

1. _____

2. _____

3. _____

daily celebration:

today I felt...

excited ○

happy ○

confused ○

frustrated ○

sad ○

_____ ○

standout human

of the day

today I'm grateful for...

1. _____

2. _____

3. _____

daily celebration:

today I felt...

excited ○

happy ○

confused ○

frustrated ○

sad ○

_____ ○

standout human

of the day

you
are
strong

What is a strength of yours that you often rely on? We have eyes to see, ears to hear, hands to high five! Our bodies are incredible tools for living out this beautiful life. Being grateful for our abilities allows us to have more of an appreciation for all of the wonderful things our bodies allow us to do each day.

List 10 things you are thankful your body allows you to do.

DATE: /   /

today I'm grateful for...

1. _____

2. _____

3. _____

daily celebration:

today I felt...

excited ◯

happy ◯

confused ◯

frustrated ◯

sad ◯

_____ ◯

standout human

of the day

today I'm grateful for...

1. _____
2. _____
3. _____

daily celebration:

today I felt...

excited ○
happy ○
confused ○
frustrated ○
sad ○
_____ ○

standout human

of the day

DATE: /   /

today I'm grateful for...

1. _____

2. _____

3. _____

daily celebration:

today I felt...

excited ◯

happy ◯

confused ◯

frustrated ◯

sad ◯

_____ ◯

standout human

of the day

today I'm grateful for...

1. _____
2. _____
3. _____

daily celebration:

today I felt...

excited ◯
happy ◯
confused ◯
frustrated ◯
sad ◯
_____ ◯

standout human
of the day

DATE: /   /

today I'm grateful for...

1. _____

2. _____

3. _____

daily celebration:

today I felt...

excited ◯

happy ◯

confused ◯

frustrated ◯

sad ◯

_____ ◯

standout human

_____

of the day

today I'm grateful for...

1. _____

2. _____

3. _____

**daily
celebration:**

today I felt...

excited ◯

happy ◯

confused ◯

frustrated ◯

sad ◯

_____ ◯

standout human

of the day

DATE: ___ / ___ / _____

today I'm grateful for...

1. _____

2. _____

3. _____

daily celebration:

today I felt...

excited ◯

happy ◯

confused ◯

frustrated ◯

sad ◯

_____ ◯

standout human

of the day

today I'm grateful for...

1. _____

2. _____

3. _____

daily celebration:

today I felt...

excited ◯

happy ◯

confused ◯

frustrated ◯

sad ◯

_____ ◯

standout human

of the day

DATE: /   /

today I'm grateful for...

1. _____

2. _____

3. _____

daily celebration:

today I felt...

excited ○

happy ○

confused ○

frustrated ○

sad ○

_____ ○

standout human
of the day

today I'm grateful for...

1. _____

2. _____

3. _____

daily
celebration:

today I felt...

excited ◯

happy ◯

confused ◯

frustrated ◯

sad ◯

_____ ◯

standout human
of the day

Time to take a quick pause! Go outside. Take a deep breath. Exhale slowly. Notice the beauty of the natural world around you and soak it in.

Life gets busy and if we let ourselves get wrapped up in the routine of school and sports and friendships and extracurriculars, we miss out on small beauties all around us, whether it be a patch of flowers, a kind greeting from a neighbor or a calming moment free of noise.

Challenge yourself to go on a walk around your neighborhood this week. Leave your phone at home and allow yourself to be fully present outside.

DATE: / /

today I'm grateful for...

1. _____
2. _____
3. _____

daily celebration:

today I felt...

excited ◯
happy ◯
confused ◯
frustrated ◯
sad ◯
_____ ◯

standout human
_____
of the day

today I'm grateful for...

1. _____
2. _____
3. _____

daily celebration:

today I felt...

excited ◯
happy ◯
confused ◯
frustrated ◯
sad ◯
_____ ◯

standout human of the day

DATE: /   /

today I'm grateful for...

1. _____

2. _____

3. _____

daily celebration:

today I felt...

excited ⭕

happy ⭕

confused ⭕

frustrated ⭕

sad ⭕

_____ ⭕

standout human

of the day

today I'm grateful for...

1. _____

2. _____

3. _____

daily celebration:

today I felt...

excited ○

happy ○

confused ○

frustrated ○

sad ○

_____ ○

standout human

_____

of the day

DATE: /   /

today I'm grateful for...

1. _____

2. _____

3. _____

daily
celebration:

today I felt...

excited   ◯

happy   ◯

confused   ◯

frustrated   ◯

sad   ◯

_____   ◯

standout human

of the day

DATE: / /

today I'm grateful for...

1. _____

2. _____

3. _____

daily celebration:

today I felt...

excited ◯

happy ◯

confused ◯

frustrated ◯

sad ◯

_____ ◯

standout human

of the day

DATE: /   /

today I'm grateful for...

1. _____

2. _____

3. _____

daily celebration:

today I felt...

excited ○

happy ○

confused ○

frustrated ○

sad ○

_____ ○

standout human

of the day

today I'm grateful for...

1. _____

2. _____

3. _____

daily celebration:

today I felt...

excited ○

happy ○

confused ○

frustrated ○

sad ○

_____ ○

standout human of the day

DATE: /   /

today I'm grateful for...

1. _____
2. _____
3. _____

daily celebration:

today I felt...

excited ◯
happy ◯
confused ◯
frustrated ◯
sad ◯
_____ ◯

standout human
of the day

today I'm grateful for...

1. _____

2. _____

3. _____

daily celebration:

today I felt...

excited ○

happy ○

confused ○

frustrated ○

sad ○

_____ ○

standout human

of the day

do it

for

~~yourself~~

others

Selflessness [n] : the act of being more concerned with the needs of those around you, rather than your own.

When we occupy our minds with the struggles and challenges in our own life, it is easy to get down. Studies have shown that a single selfless act increases your sense of connectedness and decreases feelings of loneliness and sadness. This mental shift, in turn, creates a greater sense of gratitude.

Choose one person to focus your attention on and find a way to meet one need you see in their life. Journal about how it made you feel.

DATE: /   /

today I'm grateful for...

1. _____

2. _____

3. _____

daily celebration:

today I felt...

excited ○

happy ○

confused ○

frustrated ○

sad ○

_____ ○

standout human

_____

of the day

today I'm grateful for...

1. _____

2. _____

3. _____

daily celebration:

today I felt...

excited ◯

happy ◯

confused ◯

frustrated ◯

sad ◯

_____ ◯

standout human
of the day

DATE: / /

today I'm grateful for...

1. _____
2. _____
3. _____

daily celebration:

today I felt...

excited ◯
happy ◯
confused ◯
frustrated ◯
sad ◯
_____ ◯

standout human
of the day

today I'm grateful for...

1. _____

2. _____

3. _____

daily celebration:

today I felt...

excited ◯

happy ◯

confused ◯

frustrated ◯

sad ◯

_____ ◯

standout human

of the day

DATE: /   /

today I'm grateful for...

1. _____

2. _____

3. _____

daily celebration:

today I felt...

excited ◯

happy ◯

confused ◯

frustrated ◯

sad ◯

_____ ◯

standout human

of the day

today I'm grateful for...

1. _____

2. _____

3. _____

daily celebration:

today I felt...

excited ◯

happy ◯

confused ◯

frustrated ◯

sad ◯

_____ ◯

standout human

_____

of the day

DATE: ___ / ___ / ___

today I'm grateful for...

1. _____
2. _____
3. _____

daily celebration:

today I felt...

excited ⭕
happy ⭕
confused ⭕
frustrated ⭕
sad ⭕
_____ ⭕

standout human
_____
of the day

today I'm grateful for...

1. _____

2. _____

3. _____

daily celebration:

today I felt...

excited ◯

happy ◯

confused ◯

frustrated ◯

sad ◯

_____ ◯

standout human
of the day

DATE: /   /

today I'm grateful for...

1. _____

2. _____

3. _____

daily celebration:

today I felt...

excited ○

happy ○

confused ○

frustrated ○

sad ○

_____ ○

standout human

of the day

DATE: ___ / ___ / ___

today I'm grateful for...

1. _____

2. _____

3. _____

daily celebration:

today I felt...

excited ◯

happy ◯

confused ◯

frustrated ◯

sad ◯

_____ ◯

standout human of the day

savor the good.

There are moments in our lives where we feel a true and genuine sense of gratitude and our instant response is one of "wow, this is awesome!" or "how great is that!" Those times are a moment of true and absolute thankfulness. The next time you experience that feeling, pause and soak it in. Savor that goodness the moment that it happens.

Use this page to write about a moment of genuine gratitude the next time it happens!

DATE: / /

today I'm grateful for...

1. _____
2. _____
3. _____

daily celebration:

today I felt...

excited ◯
happy ◯
confused ◯
frustrated ◯
sad ◯
_____ ◯

standout human

_____

of the day

DATE: / /

today I'm grateful for...

1. _____

2. _____

3. _____

daily celebration:

today I felt...

excited ◯

happy ◯

confused ◯

frustrated ◯

sad ◯

_____ ◯

standout human

of the day

DATE: /   /

---

today I'm grateful for...

1. _____

2. _____

3. _____

---

daily celebration:

---

today I felt...

excited ◯

happy ◯

confused ◯

frustrated ◯

sad ◯

_____ ◯

standout human

of the day

today I'm grateful for...

1. _____

2. _____

3. _____

daily celebration:

today I felt...

excited ○

happy ○

confused ○

frustrated ○

sad ○

_____ ○

standout human
of the day

DATE: /   /

today I'm grateful for...

1. _____

2. _____

3. _____

daily celebration:

today I felt...

excited ◯

happy ◯

confused ◯

frustrated ◯

sad ◯

_____ ◯

standout human

of the day

today I'm grateful for...

1. _____

2. _____

3. _____

daily celebration:

today I felt...

excited ○

happy ○

confused ○

frustrated ○

sad ○

_____ ○

standout human

of the day

DATE: /   /

today I'm grateful for...

1. _____

2. _____

3. _____

daily celebration:

today I felt...

excited ○

happy ○

confused ○

frustrated ○

sad ○

_____ ○

standout human

_____

of the day

DATE: / /

today I'm grateful for...

1. _____

2. _____

3. _____

daily celebration:

today I felt...

excited ○
happy ○
confused ○
frustrated ○
sad ○
_____ ○

standout human
of the day

DATE: /   /

today I'm grateful for...

1. _____

2. _____

3. _____

daily celebration:

today I felt...

excited ◯

happy ◯

confused ◯

frustrated ◯

sad ◯

_____ ◯

standout human

_____

of the day

today I'm grateful for...

1. _____

2. _____

3. _____

daily celebration:

today I felt...

excited ◯

happy ◯

confused ◯

frustrated ◯

sad ◯

_____ ◯

standout human

of the day

cultivate optimism

Optimism is defined as
the tendency to look on
the more positive side
of events. We have the
power to consider the
good in all things. Bad
things do happen, and it
would be silly to pretend
otherwise. Some days
school is just plain hard;
friends are simply unkind.
But we don't have to allow
those things to effect our
outlook on life as a whole.
When we are optimistic
about life as a whole,
we are naturally more
inclined to be grateful for
all the small things.

**When things don't go your
way this week,**

DATE: ___ / ___ / ___

today I'm grateful for...

1. _____

2. _____

3. _____

daily celebration:

today I felt...

excited ○

happy ○

confused ○

frustrated ○

sad ○

_____ ○

standout human

_____

of the day

today I'm grateful for...

1. _____

2. _____

3. _____

daily celebration:

today I felt...

excited ○

happy ○

confused ○

frustrated ○

sad ○

_____ ○

standout human

of the day

DATE: /   /

today I'm grateful for...

1. _____

2. _____

3. _____

daily celebration:

.

today I felt...

excited ◯

happy ◯

confused ◯

frustrated ◯

sad ◯

_____ ◯

standout human
_____
of the day

DATE: /   /

today I'm grateful for...

1. _____

2. _____

3. _____

daily celebration:

today I felt...

excited ◯

happy ◯

confused ◯

frustrated ◯

sad ◯

_____ ◯

standout human

of the day

DATE: /   /

today I'm grateful for...

1. _____

2. _____

3. _____

daily celebration:

today I felt...

excited ◯

happy ◯

confused ◯

frustrated ◯

sad ◯

_____ ◯

standout human

of the day

today I'm grateful for...

1. _____

2. _____

3. _____

daily celebration:

today I felt...

excited ○

happy ○

confused ○

frustrated ○

sad ○

_____ ○

standout human

_____

of the day

DATE: / /

today I'm grateful for...

1. _____

2. _____

3. _____

daily celebration:

today I felt...

excited ◯

happy ◯

confused ◯

frustrated ◯

sad ◯

_____ ◯

standout human
_____
of the day

DATE: / /

today I'm grateful for...

1. _____

2. _____

3. _____

daily celebration:

today I felt...

excited ○
happy ○
confused ○
frustrated ○
sad ○
_____ ○

standout human
of the day

DATE: /   /

today I'm grateful for...

1. _____

2. _____

3. _____

daily celebration:

today I felt...

excited ◯

happy ◯

confused ◯

frustrated ◯

sad ◯

_____ ◯

standout human

of the day

today I'm grateful for...

1. _____

2. _____

3. _____

daily celebration:

today I felt...

excited ◯

happy ◯

confused ◯

frustrated ◯

sad ◯

_____ ◯

standout human
of the day

rooted in
gratitude

Life will always throw
unexpected obstacles
at you. Whether its a
pop quiz, difficult family
dynamics, or losing a
big game that you've
trained for all year. These
challenges can leave
us feeling completely
uprooted if we have not
grounded ourselves in
truth.

The small practice of daily
gratitude now will serve
as our truths during those
times of chaos. **Keep
putting the work in!**

DATE: /   /

today I'm grateful for...

1. _____
2. _____
3. _____

daily celebration:

today I felt...

excited ○
happy ○
confused ○
frustrated ○
sad ○
_____ ○

standout human

of the day

today I'm grateful for...

1. _____

2. _____

3. _____

daily celebration:

today I felt...

excited ◯

happy ◯

confused ◯

frustrated ◯

sad ◯

_____ ◯

standout human

_____

of the day

DATE: /   /

today I'm grateful for...

1. _____

2. _____

3. _____

daily celebration:

today I felt...

excited ○

happy ○

confused ○

frustrated ○

sad ○

_____ ○

standout human

_____

of the day

today I'm grateful for...

1. _____

2. _____

3. _____

daily celebration:

today I felt...

excited ○

happy ○

confused ○

frustrated ○

sad ○

_____ ○

standout human
_____
of the day

DATE: ___ / ___ / ___

today I'm grateful for...

1. _____

2. _____

3. _____

daily
celebration:

today I felt...

excited ◯

happy ◯

confused ◯

frustrated ◯

sad ◯

_____ ◯

standout human
of the day

today I'm grateful for...

1. _____

2. _____

3. _____

daily celebration:

today I felt...

excited ◯

happy ◯

confused ◯

frustrated ◯

sad ◯

_____ ◯

standout human

of the day

DATE: _____ / _____ / _____

today I'm grateful for...

1. _____

2. _____

3. _____

daily celebration:

today I felt...

excited ◯

happy ◯

confused ◯

frustrated ◯

sad ◯

_____ ◯

standout human _____ *of the day*

today I'm grateful for...

1. _____

2. _____

3. _____

daily celebration:

today I felt...

excited ◯

happy ◯

confused ◯

frustrated ◯

sad ◯

_____ ◯

standout human

_____

of the day

DATE: /   /

today I'm grateful for...

1. _____

2. _____

3. _____

daily celebration:

today I felt...

excited ◯

happy ◯

confused ◯

frustrated ◯

sad ◯

_____ ◯

standout human
of the day

today I'm grateful for...

1. _____

2. _____

3. _____

daily celebration:

today I felt...

excited ○

happy ○

confused ○

frustrated ○

sad ○

_____ ○

standout human

of the day

smile

Ready for your simplest challenge of all? SMILE! Smile more often and bigger and longer. A smile, genuine or forces, results in happiness, not only for yourself but people around you. That happiness in turn creates a sense of gratitude in your life.

Whenever you catch someone's eye in the hallway today, be the first one to smile. Everyone enjoys a friendly face. Write about how it made you feel.

DATE: /   /

today I'm grateful for...

1. _____

2. _____

3. _____

daily celebration:

today I felt...

excited ⃝

happy ⃝

confused ⃝

frustrated ⃝

sad ⃝

_____ ⃝

standout human of the day

today I'm grateful for...

1. _____

2. _____

3. _____

daily celebration:

today I felt...

excited ◯

happy ◯

confused ◯

frustrated ◯

sad ◯

_____ ◯

standout human

_____

of the day

DATE: /   /

today I'm grateful for...

1. _____

2. _____

3. _____

daily celebration:

today I felt...

excited ◯

happy ◯

confused ◯

frustrated ◯

sad ◯

_____ ◯

standout human

of the day

today I'm grateful for...

1. _____

2. _____

3. _____

daily celebration:

today I felt...

excited ◯

happy ◯

confused ◯

frustrated ◯

sad ◯

_____ ◯

standout human of the day

DATE: ___ / ___ / _____

today I'm grateful for...

1. _____

2. _____

3. _____

daily
celebration:

today I felt...

excited ◯

happy ◯

confused ◯

frustrated ◯

sad ◯

_____ ◯

standout human
of the day

DATE: / /

today I'm grateful for...

1. _____

2. _____

3. _____

daily celebration:

today I felt...

excited ◯

happy ◯

confused ◯

frustrated ◯

sad ◯

_____ ◯

standout human

of the day

DATE: /   /

today I'm grateful for...

1. _____

2. _____

3. _____

daily celebration:

today I felt...

excited ⃝

happy ⃝

confused ⃝

frustrated ⃝

sad ⃝

_____ ⃝

standout human

_____

of the day

today I'm grateful for...

1. _____

2. _____

3. _____

daily celebration:

today I felt...

excited ○

happy ○

confused ○

frustrated ○

sad ○

_____ ○

standout human

_____

of the day

DATE: /   /

today I'm grateful for...

1. _____

2. _____

3. _____

daily celebration:

today I felt...

excited ◯

happy ◯

confused ◯

frustrated ◯

sad ◯

_____ ◯

standout human

of the day

today I'm grateful for...

1. _____

2. _____

3. _____

daily
celebration:

today I felt...

excited ⚪

happy ⚪

confused ⚪

frustrated ⚪

sad ⚪

_____ ⚪

standout human
of the day

Congratulations!

You made it through 90 days of daily gratitude. An A plus for you! We hope this journal has taught you a bit more about how to develop a practice of gratitude in your life, from big ways to small. Keep on smiling!

good days start with gratitude